Floral Designs
COLOR BY NUMBER COLORING BOOK

Jessica Mazurkiewicz

Dover Publications, Inc.
Mineola, New York

Bibliographical Note

Floral Designs Color by Number Coloring Book, first published by Dover Publications, Inc., in 2015, is a revised edition of the work originally published by Dover in 2014.

This 2015 edition printed for Barnes & Noble, Inc., by Dover Publications, Inc.

International Standard Book Number

ISBN-13: 978-0-486-80385-2
ISBN-10: 0-486-80385-6

Manufactured in the United States by Courier Corporation

This coloring collection features full-page floral designs for you to color. Each plate is shown in full-color on the inside covers. You can duplicate these images simply by following the color guide found on the inside front cover, or choose your own colors for a more personal touch. As part of Dover's *Creative Haven* series for the experienced colorist, each plate is highly detailed, and enclosed in a border for a finished look. Plus, perforated, unbacked pages offer you the opportunity to experiment with any media you like, and make displaying your work easy!

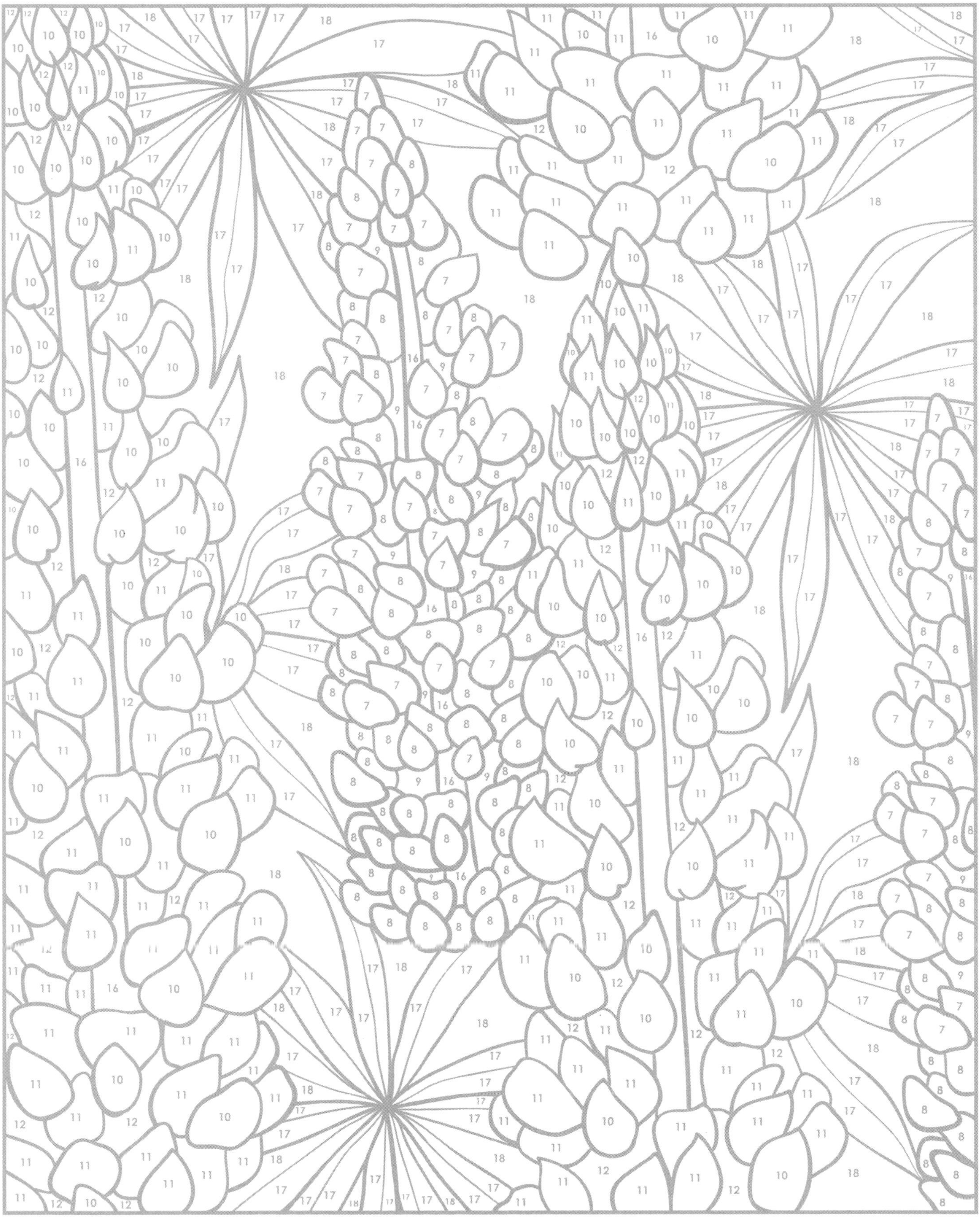